Pig's
farm

Sheep's
farm

Minnow's
farm

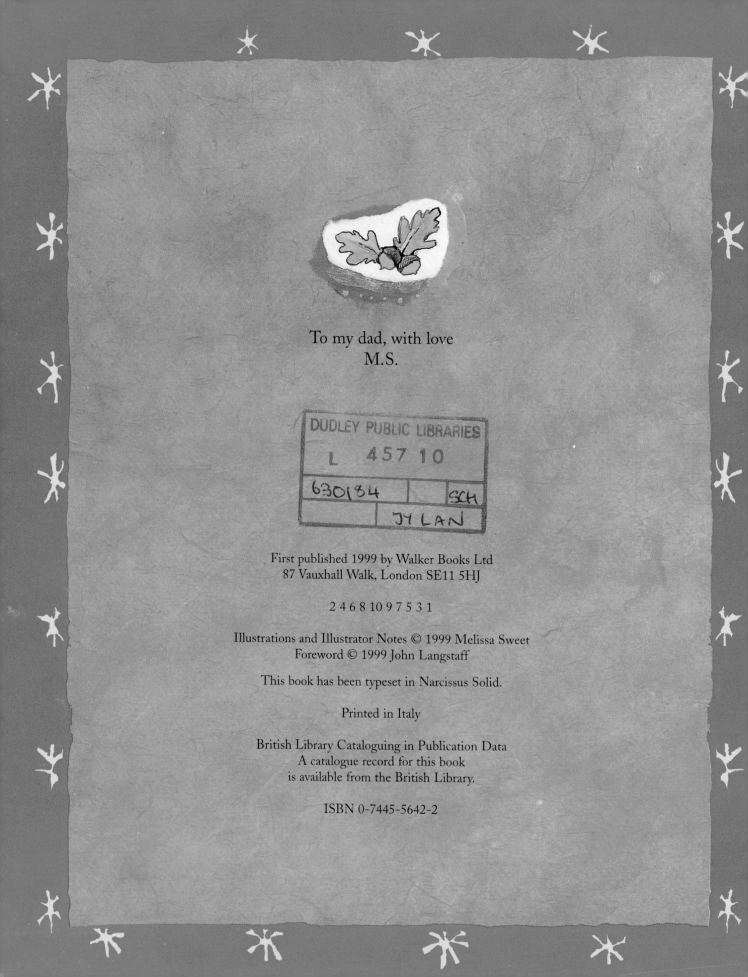

To my dad, with love
M.S.

First published 1999 by Walker Books Ltd
87 Vauxhall Walk, London SE11 5HJ

2 4 6 8 10 9 7 5 3 1

Illustrations and Illustrator Notes © 1999 Melissa Sweet
Foreword © 1999 John Langstaff

This book has been typeset in Narcissus Solid.

Printed in Italy

British Library Cataloguing in Publication Data
A catalogue record for this book
is available from the British Library.

ISBN 0-7445-5642-2

A farmyard carol

On Christmas Day in the Morning

illustrated by

Melissa Sweet

WALKER BOOKS
AND SUBSIDIARIES
LONDON · BOSTON · SYDNEY

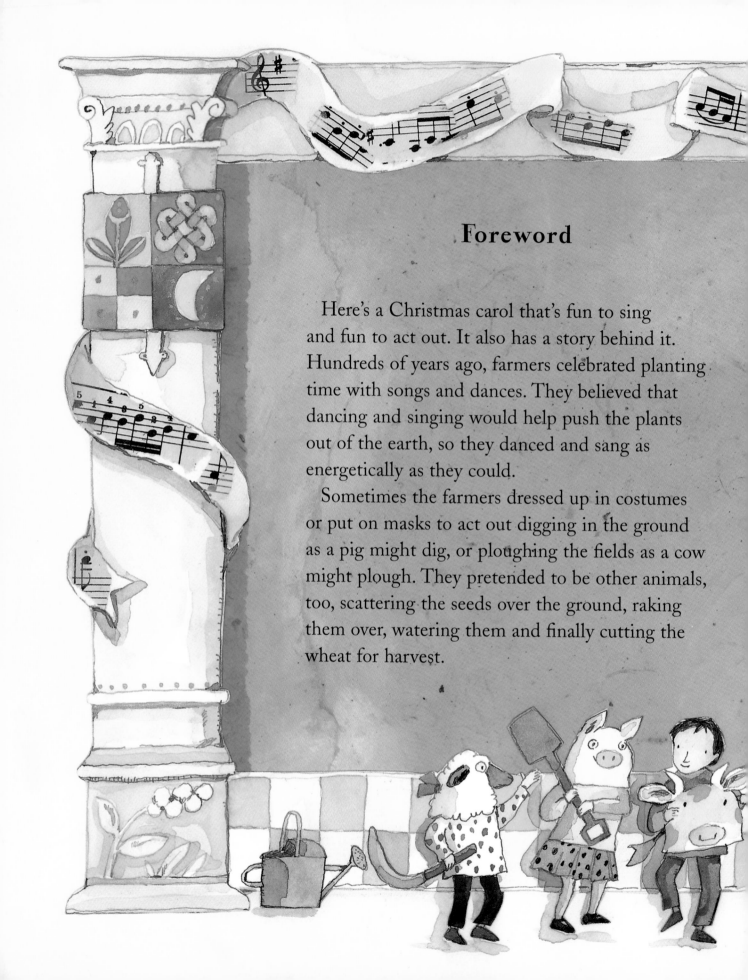

Foreword

Here's a Christmas carol that's fun to sing
and fun to act out. It also has a story behind it.
Hundreds of years ago, farmers celebrated planting
time with songs and dances. They believed that
dancing and singing would help push the plants
out of the earth, so they danced and sang as
energetically as they could.

Sometimes the farmers dressed up in costumes
or put on masks to act out digging in the ground
as a pig might dig, or ploughing the fields as a cow
might plough. They pretended to be other animals,
too, scattering the seeds over the ground, raking
them over, watering them and finally cutting the
wheat for harvest.

You can do all those things yourself, just as the farmers did. Move around and imitate the animals you're singing about in each verse. The strong rhythm of the song will tell you how to move. You might like to make up your own verses, too. It's easy. Just match the name of an animal to an action you can think of. The fun is trying to find words that rhyme, that have the same sound.

This traditional song was first written down by a woman called Lucy Broadwood. She learnt it from a farmer who sang it for her more than one hundred years ago. Lucy Broadwood called it "There Was a Pig Went Out to Dig", and it is thanks to her that we can sing it today.

JOHN LANGSTAFF

There was a pig
went out to dig,
On Christmas Day,
On Christmas Day.
There was a pig
Went out to dig
On Christmas Day
In the morning!

There was a cow
Went out to plough,
On Christmas Day,
On Christmas Day.
There was a cow
Went out to plough
On Christmas Day
In the morning!

There was a sparrow
went out to harrow,
On Christmas Day,
On Christmas Day.
There was a sparrow
Went out to harrow
On Christmas Day
In the morning!

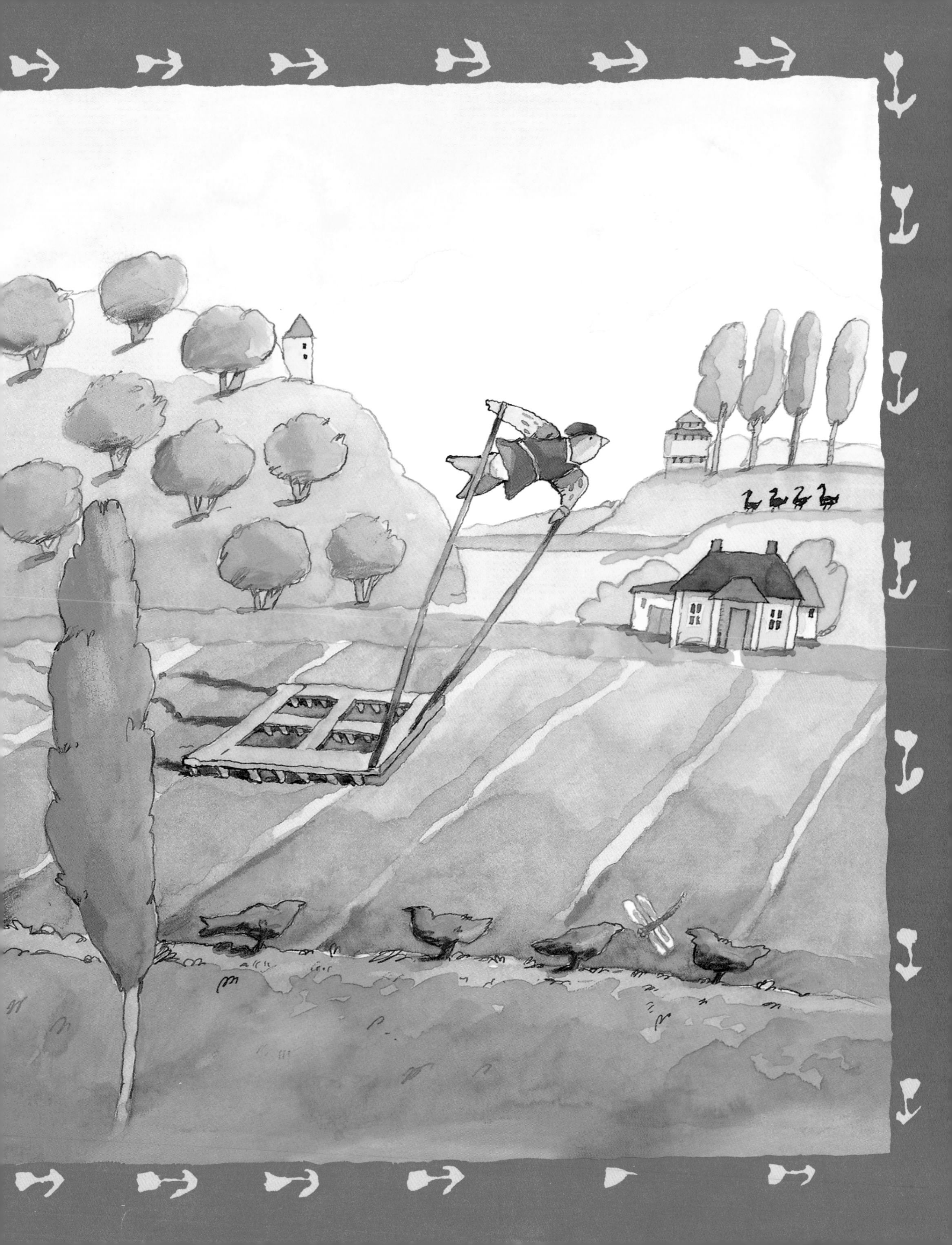

There was a crow
went out to sow,
On Christmas Day,
On Christmas Day.
There was a crow
Went out to sow
On Christmas Day
In the morning!

There was a sheep
went out to reap,
On Christmas Day,
On Christmas Day.
There was a sheep
Went out to reap
On Christmas Day
In the morning!

There was a drake
went out to rake,
On Christmas Day,
On Christmas Day.
There was a drake
Went out to rake
On Christmas Day
In the morning!

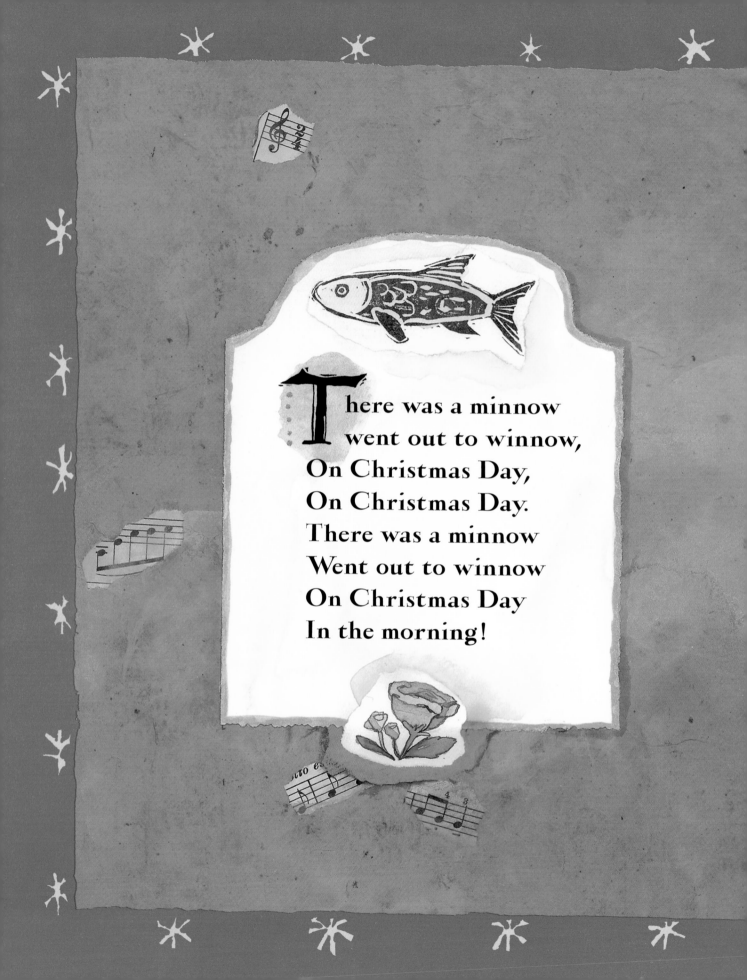

There was a minnow
Went out to winnow,
On Christmas Day,
On Christmas Day.
There was a minnow
Went out to winnow
On Christmas Day
In the morning!

Then every beast prepared the feast,
On Christmas Day, on Christmas Day.

Then every beast prepared the feast
On Christmas Day in the morning!

Let every creature on Earth now sing,
On Christmas Day,
On Christmas Day.
Let every creature on Earth now sing
On Christmas Day in the morning!

Christmas Day

There was a pig went out to dig, Chris - i - mas Day,

Chris - i - mas Day. There was a pig went out to dig On

Chris - i - mas Day in the morn - ing!

There was a cow went out to plough...

There was a sparrow went out to harrow...

There was a crow went out to sow...

There was a sheep went out to reap...

There was a drake went out to rake...

There was a minnow went out to winnow...

∾ Illustrator Notes ∾

In preparation for illustrating *On Christmas Day in the Morning*, I researched the many symbols and images associated with the Christmas season. These rich symbols, drawn from nature, agriculture and the cycle of seasons, had their beginnings long before the birth of Jesus Christ, and continue to remind us of joy, abundance and rebirth.

Mistletoe   Mistletoe was sacred to the Norse goddess of love and marriage, Frigga. It is neither tree nor shrub, but a plant that grows and seeds itself in the branches of trees, never touching the ground. It is still considered good luck to be kissed beneath mistletoe.

Oak   To the Celtic and Norse people, the oak tree was a sacred symbol that represented regeneration, rebirth and endurance. During the winter solstice, when the branches were bare, Celts decorated oak trees with gilded apples and candles.

Holly   Long ago, people believed that the leaves of holly remained green and the berries red throughout the year so that the world would still be beautiful even after other trees had dropped their leaves.

Laurel The Ancient Romans used laurel (or sweet bay) during the winter Saturnalia celebration as a symbol of triumph and eternity because when the plant dies, its leaves do not wilt. The Romans made wreaths of laurel and hung them from their doorways during winter, a practice that carried on after the spread of Christianity.

Christmas Rose The Christmas Rose is an actual rose native to the mountains of central Europe, where it blooms in winter. Three roses gathered together symbolize light, love and life.

Pomegranate In Ancient Greece, the pomegranate fruit was associated with Persephone, the goddess who brought the spring each year. Because the pomegranate is full of seeds, it symbolized fertility and represented a return of life, as well as boundless love.

Wheat I've used a sheaf of wheat as a reminder of the yearly work of growing and harvesting carried out by labourers in the fields. It was and continues to be an apt symbol for Earth's bounty and life's abundance.

Crow's
farm

Cow's
farm

Sparrow's
farm

Drake's
farm